CAPTAIN COURAGE AND THE ROSE STREET GANG

JAN MARK

Additional Material
Stephen Cockett

Series Consultant
Cecily O'Neill

CollinsEducational
An imprint of HarperCollins*Publishers*

Copyright © 1987 Jan Mark, Playscript
Stephen Cockett, End material

First published 1987, reprinted 1989,
reprinted 1991
ISBN 0 00 330235 0

Cartoons by Richard Thompson (Rich)

Design and artwork by Andrew McColm and
Richard Cox

Acknowledgements
pp. 43-44 reprinted with permission of Curtis
Brown, Ltd; Adapted from OUT THERE,
Copyright © 1971 by Adrien Stoutenburg.
p. 52 from 'On line interrogation of hospital
patients by a time-sharing terminal with
computer/consultant comparison analysis'
published by the Institution of Electrical
Engineers, September 1970. pp. 54-56 "The
Fun They Had" from EARTH IS ROOM
ENOUGH by Isaac Asimov. Reprinted by
permission of Doubleday & Company, Inc.
p. 58 reprinted with permission of the estate
of the late Sonia Brownell Orwell, Secker &
Warburg Ltd.

Photographs
Front cover and p. 38, David Hoffman,
p. 39 Sally and Richard Greenhill.

Typeset by CG Graphic Services, Tring, Herts
Reproduced, printed and bound in Great Britain
by Bell and Bain, Glasgow.

CONTENTS

THE CHARACTERS

The Rose Street Gang:
  Arthur Cooper (Arty)
  Lancelot Cooper (Lance)
  Beowulf Hopkins
  Kay
  Guinever
  Enid
Captain Courage – a hologram
Mrs Cooper
Mrs Hopkins
Senior Citizen
Shopping Area Attendant
Level Tenner 1
Level Tenner 2
Factcentre Announcers (eight)
PREM – a chessplaying robot

Senior citizens
Passers-by
Level Tenners

*The play is in two acts and takes place in the Rose Street
Development between Saturday morning and Sunday
morning. It is summer, although there is no way of knowing
this: the Development is fully air-conditioned and artificially
lit. There are no windows as such.*

CAPTAIN COURAGE AND THE ROSE STREET GANG

Act One
SCENE ONE

*The **Coopers'** housing unit. **Lance** and **Arty** are in the leisure area, where **Lance** is playing chess with **PREM**, his Programmed Response Module. **PREM** is malfunctioning and edges crabwise round the chess board every time it makes a move. **Lance** follows it. **Mum** is in the utility area doing the washing in the home laundry unit. **Arty** is getting in the way.*

ARTY   I want to play in the street.

MRS COOPER   For heaven's sake, stop whining and get out from under my feet.

LANCE   *to **PREM*** Your move.   *He hits it*   Your move!

ARTY   Lance, why don't we go and play in the street?

LANCE   Too far. Anyway, it may be raining.

ARTY   I bet it's not.

LANCE   It may be by the time we get there. Check.

*Arty goes to the **Factcentre**, a large television screen with an extensive console. He presses buttons.*

FACTCENTRE 1   What service do you require, Dataseeker?

ARTY   Weather forecast.

FACTCENTRE 2   Good morning, Dataseeker. The weather prospects in your area are good. Congratulations. This certainly looks like being a bright weekend for all you fortunate Maidstoneites. The forecast for today, and tomorrow *and* Monday is bright –

1

FACTCENTRE 3   – and a Party Political Broadcast on behalf of the Kent County Council –

ARTY   Weather! *He hits it*

FACTCENTRE 2   – is bright sunshine and occasional fog patches over low-lying coastal areas around nightfall. The outlook –

FACTCENTRE 4   – currently retailing at ninety-five pounds with a discount for holders of a Platinum Euro-Bond user's card –

LANCE   Give it a kick. Checkmate.

FACTCENTRE 2   – a slight breeze from the South-West should keep you comfortably cool. Thank you for calling. Have a nice day.

FACTCENTRE 1   Thank you for calling, Dataseeker. Have a nice day.

ARTY   There you are. It's not raining.

LANCE   I don't trust that thing. For all you know that could be last week's forecast. No one's going to bother to find out, are they? They couldn't prove anything if they did.   *To* ***PREM***   I said checkmate.

ARTY   What's the point of being the Rose Street Gang if we never play in the street? We might just as well call ourselves the Walkway Mob or the Level Eleveners.

LANCE   And get mistaken for the Level Tenners? Not likely. Look, PREM, you're beaten. Why not give up? Anyway, no one would be able to say it. Level Eleveners . . . Levelelevevers . . . Evelenevelers . . . Levenevenerels . . . It's a tongue-twister.

PREM *is sidling towards the door.* ***Lance*** *goes after it.*

LANCE   Come out of there. Can't bear losing . . .

ARTY   You said we could play in the street when summer came.

LANCE   I don't feel like it; it's too much hassle getting there . . . Suppose we *did* meet the Level Tenners? Anyway, I'm going down to Beowulf's. He was getting a new hologram for his birthday. D'you want to come?

ARTY   I suppose so. It doesn't look like we're going to do anything else, does it?

2

LANCE *putting PREM into the storage unit* Come on, then.

MRS COOPER *yelling* Where are you off to?

LANCE Just down to Beowulf's.

MRS COOPER What about lunch?

LANCE We'll be back for dinner.

MRS COOPER *giving him a lunch box* You'd better take these in case you want a snack. The labels have peeled off ... you might as well finish them up.

ARTY What are they?

MRS COOPER Well, you won't know till you've eaten them, will you?

ARTY *picking the loose labels out of the box* Crunchy Haddock Bites ... Cripsy Banana fries ... Flaky Praties ... Spicy Nibbles ... *Glumly* I don't suppose we'll know even *after* we've eaten them.

*He follows **Lance** out of the door. **Mum** goes back to the home laundry unit, which is leaking, and kicks it.*

SCENE TWO

*The Walkway. **Arty** and **Lance** are just approaching **Beowulf**'s housing unit, next to the Hydroponic Memorial Facility. This is an artificial garden made to look like a small tropical island ('hydroponics' is the art of growing plants in water with chemicals).*

ARTY *Why* can't we play in the street?

LANCE Oh, for crying out loud! Look, I want to see this hologram.

ARTY Well, afterwards, then. They were saying, down the education centre, that it wasn't a *real* hologram.

LANCE It's better than a hologram, Dumbo, it's an autogram. Real up-to-the-nano-second stuff; it works without a plate. Not like that rubbishy old thing we've got.

ARTY I wish it wasn't so far to Beowulf's.

LANCE It's a sight farther down to the street.

ARTY Why can't he come to ours, for once?

LANCE   You know what his mum's like – she thinks our end of the Walkway's rough.

ARTY   I suppose that means she thinks *we're* rough, too.

LANCE   She ought to see what goes on down *their* end of the Walkway after dark.

*They have reached **Beowulf**'s place. **Lance** presses a button on the entryphone.*

MRS HOPKINS   *from inside*   Now who is it?

LANCE   *very polite*   It's Lance and Arty Cooper, Mrs Hopkins. Do you think we could possibly see Beowulf, if it's convenient?   *To **Arty***   Butter the old hag up.

***Mrs Hopkins** opens the front door, suspiciously.*

MRS HOPKINS   I hope your shoes are clean. Really, the things that get left lying around on these walkways . . . What the Hygiene Department are thinking of letting the place get into this state . . .

***Lance** and **Arty** look at the soles of their shoes before following her through the door.*

SCENE THREE

*Inside the **Hopkins'** housing unit. A hallway leads into the main area.*

MRS HOPKINS   Mind where you walk – don't go near that wet paint. Mr Hopkins is making modifications.

LANCE   *to **Arty***   *Again?* He's had this place inside out . . .

MRS HOPKINS   Careful of the plaster, Beowulf's in the living room.

ARTY   The living room?

MRS HOPKINS   *heavily superior*   I suppose *you'd* call it the leisure area.   *She heads for the utility area*   'Room' sounds so much *nicer*, I always think.

ARTY   *to himself*   Wonder if they've got a *dying* room, too?

*They go into the living room. It is just like the **Coopers'** leisure area but more ornate. One wall is occupied by the **Factcentre**. **Beowulf** is sitting on the floor, fiddling with keys on a hand-held control module.*

LANCE   Happy birthday. Where is it, then?

BEOWULF   *irritably*   Where's what, then?   *He bangs the module against his knee*

LANCE   The autogram; did you get it?

BEOWULF   *poking the module*   In here, I suppose; only I can't get the bleeder out. I've only seen him once. He went on the blink as soon as he appeared.

ARTY   He?

BEOWULF   It's a person. Supposed to be.

LANCE   Let's have a look.

BEOWULF   Looking won't help. It's malfunctioning.

LANCE   So what isn't?

They bend over the module. **Arty** *goes to the* **Factcentre** *and presses keys.*

FACTCENTRE 1   What service do you require, Dataseeker?

ARTY   Adscan.

FACTCENTRE 5   Adscan at your service, Dataseeker. Which classification do you require?

ARTY   Retail Leisure Aids.

FACTCENTRE 2   Good morning, Dataseeker.The weather prospects in your area are good. Congratulations. This certainly looks like being –

ARTY   *hitting keys*   Retail Leisure Aids.

FACTCENTRE 3   This is a party Political Broadcast on behalf –

ARTY   RETAIL LEISURE AIDS!

LANCE   Kick it.

FACTCENTRE 6   Which facility do you require, Dataseeker?

ARTY   Autograms.

FACTCENTRE 7   . . . a significant advance over the old-fashioned hologram. Parents! Can you afford to let your children be without this important educational development? See, in Living 3D, Notable People from Living History or, at a more advantageous price, Men and Women in the Street through the Ages. Choose from Neanderthal

Man, a Roman Legionary, a Medieval Serf, a Seventeenth Century Cavalier –

FACTCENTRE 8 Get a Roundhead to match! Big reduction for the pair!

FACTCENTRE 7 – an Eighteenth Century Hussar –

FACTCENTRE 8 Can you afford to miss the horse, for *added realism*?

FACTCENTRE 7 – a Nineteenth Century Grandmother and a Twentieth Century Commando . . .

*They carry on like this in the background. **Factcentres 2, 3** and **4** break in at intervals.*

ARTY Which one have you got?

BEOWULF Twentieth Century Commando, I *suppose*. He wasn't around long enough to find out. *He kicks a gift box towards **Arty*** Captain Courage.

LANCE Quick! There he is!

***Captain Courage** appears in the corner. There is definitely a malfunction. He sidles about, one leg shorter than the other, head drawn down to one shoulder, bobbing and dipping.*

ARTY What's it meant to do?

BEOWULF It's meant to talk, for a start. *He snatches the module from **Lance** and presses a key* Oi! You!

CAPTAIN COURAGE Oooaaahooowohowooaaah . . .

ARTY *politely* What's your name?

BEOWULF It should only respond to my voice. It's personalized. *Slowly, as if to an idiot* What–is–your–name?

CAPTAIN COURAGE Whaaaa? *He twitches*

BEOWULF Your name! Your handle! Your monicker!

ARTY He doesn't look much like the picture on the box, does he? His head's all twisted.

LANCE That's meant to be a menacing smile.

ARTY Under his ear?

CAPTAIN COURAGE *levelling his gun* Kitty–kitty–kitty. Nice kitty. Come to Gran.

Silence.

LANCE What's it supposed to say?

BEOWULF *reading from the box* Drop your Kalashnikov or I'll blow you away.

CAPTAIN COURAGE *Who's* a pretty boy, then?

Beowulf hurls the control module at the wall. Captain Courage warps and flickers.

CAPTAIN COURAGE Isn't it a nice day?

ARTY Hey! That's Nineteenth Century Granny. He's been programmed with the wrong voice.

LANCE He's right. Someone else must have Granny . . . and I suppose she goes round snarling 'Drop your Kalashnikov or I'll blow you away'.

ARTY What's a Kalashnikov?

FACTCENTRE 8 Get the whole set and be the envy of your friends!

FACTCENTRE 7 Imagine, a whole cohort of Roman Soldiers!

BEOWULF Imagine, a whole cohort of Nineteenth Century Grannies!

CAPTAIN COURAGE Lovely weather for the time of year.

Every time Beowulf moves the module, the Captain moves, too, lurching and curtsying. Beowulf tries to switch off.

BEOWULF He's jammed! I can't switch him off!

CAPTAIN COURAGE How are your cauliflowers coming along?

ARTY What's a cauliflower?

BEOWULF Damn this for a lark. I'm going out. You don't catch me stuck here all day with Grandma Courage.

CAPTAIN COURAGE If you get me the wool I'll knit one for you.

LANCE What about us? I told Mum we'd be out till dinner. It's her day at the Conversation Centre. She'll have put the Security Beams on by now and we'll be locked out.

ARTY Let's go and play in the street.

BEOWULF I don't care where we play. *He strides into the utility area*

CAPTAIN COURAGE *following him* Kitty–kitty–kitty . . .

BEOWULF *to Mrs Hopkins in the utility area* We're going out, Mum.

MRS HOPKINS Stay away from the West Stairs, then.

Beowulf puts the control module on a shelf and starts to tiptoe away.

CAPTAIN COURAGE Fancy meeting you here.

MRS HOPKINS *seeing him* Get that thing out of my kitchen. It gives me the creeps.

ARTY Kitchen?

BEOWULF He's stuck at 'on'.

CAPTAIN COURAGE It's a very fine morning.

MRS HOPKINS I don't care where he's stuck as long as he's not stuck here. I don't know; as soon as you get something, you either lose it or break it.

BEOWULF OK, OK. I'll leave it in the bedroom.

CAPTAIN COURAGE *Who's* a pretty boy, then?

MRS HOPKINS No, you won't. You'll take it with you. I'm not having it hanging around here all day, talking to itself.

BEOWULF It only responds to my voice.

CAPTAIN COURAGE Where *did* I leave my umbrella?

MRS HOPKINS Take it *with* you!

Lance, Beowulf and Arty leave despondently. After a moment Captain Courage staggers after them.

SCENE FOUR

The Walkway, near the Hydroponic Memorial Facility. Several **Senior Citizens** *are dozing among the sand bags and water tanks.*

LANCE How about getting hold of some of the others?

BEOWULF What others?

CAPTAIN COURAGE Isn't it a nice day?

BEOWULF You shut up.

CAPTAIN COURAGE Kitty–kitty–kitty . . .

LANCE The rest of the Gang.

8

BEOWULF   I don't know that I want anyone to see me while *he's* around.

CAPTAIN COURAGE   How are your cauliflowers coming along?

ARTY   Never mind the others. Let's go and play in the street.

BEOWULF   What's all this with the street?

CAPTAIN COURAGE   If you get me the wool I'll knit one for you.

LANCE   He thinks that because we're the Rose Street Gang we ought to go and play in Rose Street.

ARTY   It's three years since I've been in the street. I can't hardly remember what it looks like, even.

BEOWULF   *patiently*   Look, we're the Rose Street Gang because we live in the Rose Street Development. We don't need to go out in the street.

CAPTAIN COURAGE   Where *did* I leave my umbrella?

ARTY   The Level Tenners live in the Rose Street Development too. Everyone knows they come from Level Ten. They've got identity.

BEOWULF   They've got a reputation.

CAPTAIN COURAGE   Isn't it a nice day?

BEOWULF   What price identity?

CAPTAIN COURAGE   People like you ought to be locked up.

BEOWULF   People like *you* –

LANCE   Hey, listen; when we pass the Hydro we can lose him.

BEOWULF   *whispering, so that* **Captain Courage** *can't overhear*   What? With all those old biddies sitting about? How?

LANCE   Chuck the module in among the trees. He'll follow it, won't he?

Beowulf *lobs the control module into the Hydroponic Memorial Facility.* **Captain Courage** *rises on his toes and lopes after it.*

THE CAPTAIN   Here, kitty–kitty–kitty . . .

BEOWULF   Quick! Before he notices.   *He hurries away*

LANCE   Don't be daft. He doesn't know anything.

CAPTAIN COURAGE   *to Senior Citizen*   It's a very fine morning.

The Senior Citizen has stood up and is inspecting Captain Courage suspiciously. Arty and Lance begin to tiptoe away after Beowulf. The Senior Citizen picks up the module and pursues them. Captain Courage follows, squawking odd noises.

SENIOR CITIZEN   Oi! You lot! Come back here!

LANCE   Who? Us?

SENIOR CITIZEN   Come here!

BEOWULF   It's not mine. It's nothing to do with *us.*

SENIOR CITIZEN   I saw you.

CAPTAIN COURAGE   Cauliauliauliflowowowers . . .

SENIOR CITIZEN   I saw you chuck it in. Take it away, Beowulf Hopkins, or I'll tell your dad.

The Senior Citzen hurls the control module at Beowulf and retires grumbling, to the Hydroponic Memorial Facility. Captain Courage follows the module.

BEOWULF   *picking up the module*   That's the trouble with this dump. Everyone knows everybody else.

CAPTAIN COURAGE   Lovely weather for the time of year.

ARTY   He's sort of floating, now. Like his feet don't touch the ground.

LANCE   Listen, we're going to be out all day. Let's drop by Tesco's and get some fodder. Mum gave us a load of stuff but we'll need more – and something to drink.

They set off. Captain Courage stumbles along behind them. Passers-by pause to stare curiously, and one of them points. Arty makes a rude gesture and follows the Captain.

SCENE FIVE

Tesco's is a very long coin-in-the-slot-machine. The boys move along it, putting in money and collecting goods from the service chutes underneath. Coins have to be hammered into the

10

*slots; service chutes need kicking before they will deliver. As they get ready to leave, **Beowulf** furtively slips the control module into a chute.*

BEOWULF   Get moving.

*They slip away, leaving **Captain Courage** chatting to a chewing-gum dispenser.*

CAPTAIN COURAGE   Fancy meeting you here.

*A **shopping area attendant** begins to speak to **Captain Courage**, then goes over to the service chute and takes out the control module. He starts purposefully after the boys. **Captain Courage** follows the **attendant**.*

BEOWULF   Are we going to collect the others or not?

LANCE   Don't look round now; we're being followed.

*They all stop and look round. The **attendant** and **Captain Courage** catch up.*

ATTENDANT   I saw you! Come back here! It's an offence depositing foreign articles in the service apertures. It's an offence, that is. I could get you had up for that.

`**Beowulf** takes the module. **Captain Courage** slithers up to him.`

ATTENDANT   It's always the same with you youngsters, you don't know the value of money. *He walks away, calling over his shoulder*   Wasting a perfectly good toy like that . . .

BEOWULF   *A perfectly good toy?*

CAPTAIN COURAGE   *Who's* a pretty boy, then?

ARTY   Let's go down past Level Ten, at least.

LANCE   There's a thought. Perhaps we could leave him in the elevation unit.

*They hurry away. **Captain Courage** dances after them. **Beowulf** must have said something out of earshot, for as he departs he addresses the audience.*

CAPTAIN COURAGE   Lovely weather for the time of year.

SCENE SIX

*By the lifts. A sign on the wall reads: LEVEL ELEVEN.
LOWER EAST WALKWAY. A notice propped against the lift
shafts says: ELEVATION UNITS TEMPORARILY OUT OF
ACTION. DANGER MEN AT WORK. Nearby is a row of
public telephones. Several of them carry the sign: TELECOM
UNIT OUT OF ORDER. Lance, Arty and Beowulf come in,
followed by Captain Courage. Beowulf approaches one of
the lifts and reads the sign.*

BEOWULF   No, that's no good.

CAPTAIN COURAGE   What beautiful embroidery, my
dear.

ARTY   Why do they always say Men at Work? There's never
any men at work.

LANCE   Why not drop the control module down the shaft?

BEOWULF   We'd never get near. They'll have the deterrent
beams switched on.

CAPTAIN COURAGE   If you get me the wool I'll knit one
for you.

LANCE   I don't suppose they'll be working, either. *He
approaches the lifts cautiously* Ouch! They are, though.

ARTY   We'll have to use the stairs. *Panicking* We might
meet the Level Tenners. Let's get the others, Lance. *Let's.*

LANCE   OK. If we can find a telecom that's not out of
order. *He goes to investigate*

BEOWULF   Fat chance. The coin slots are always stuffed up
with super glue or super gum.

CAPTAIN COURAGE   People like you ought to be locked
up.

ARTY   *looking at the telecom units* Spicy Nibbles make
good glue . . . but you have to chew them for ages.

LANCE   Here's one. Got any money?

ARTY   A fiver.

He gives Lance a coin. Lance dials.

LANCE   Hullo. Hullo? *yelling* HULLO! Kay! That you?
Look, Kay, we're going down the levels . . .

Arty reacts, hopefully.

12

LANCE *Down the levels!* Yeah.

- And the elevation units are U.S. We may need reinforcements.

- Interested?

- OK, bring the others.

- We'll meet you at the head of the North Stairs in half an hour.

- 'Cause it'll take us half an hour to get there, that's why. We're by the East Elevation Units.

- The East Stairs have been sealed off for months. *He hangs up* He says he'll bring Guinever and Enid. Guinever's as good as an armoured division any day.

They start to move off. **Captain Courage** *bobs behind them.*

BEOWULF When we get to the next corner, we'll lose him.

CAPTAIN COURAGE What beautiful embroidery, my dear.

ARTY What's embroidery?

LANCE My mum'd go spare if I lost something like that. They cost about three thousand each.

BEOWULF Three thousand, seven hundred and fifty, that one. My mum'll go spare, too, but she'll be even sparer if I take this loony back again.

CAPTAIN COURAGE If you get me the wool I'll knit one for you.

ARTY Perhaps your dad can mend him. He's good with his hands.

BEOWULF He'd need to be good with a hammer to get anywhere with *him*.

CAPTAIN COURAGE Isn't it a nice day?

ARTY *wistfully* He's quite good fun, really.

BEOWULF *shoving the control module into* **Arty**'s *hand* Here, you can look after him if you think so much of him. If anyone asks, he's yours.

CAPTAIN COURAGE How are your cauliflowers coming along?

ARTY What's a cauliflower?

BEOWULF Well, come on, then.

Beowulf and Lance walk away. Arty and the Captain follow, slowly.

CAPTAIN COURAGE   Where *did* I leave my umbrella?

ARTY   What's an umbrella? What's wool?

Act Two
SCENE ONE

The head of the North Stairs. A sign on the wall reads: LEVEL ELEVEN. NORTH STAIRS. Arty, Lance and Beowulf are waiting, Arty with the control module. Captain Courage hovers.

ARTY   It's quite simple, really, once you get to know him. *The others ignore him* You see, if you press *volume control*, he stands upright. *Captain Courage does his best to stand upright* *Forward Motion* makes him reach for his gun – *look* *Captain Courage reaches for his gun* and if you press *lateral hold* he throws himself flat on the ground. *Captain Courage goes down* You just have to understand him.

BEOWULF   There they are.

ARTY   Up you get.

CAPTAIN COURAGE   *getting up* Lovely weather for the time of year.

Enid, Guinever and Kay, carrying sticks, approach. Guinever gapes at Captain Courage.

GUINEVER   What in heck's that?

BEOWULF   Oh, just some old rubbish of Arty's that he picked up second hand.

CAPTAIN COURAGE   Kitty-kitty-kitty. *He draws his gun* Nice kitty. Come to Gran.

BEOWULF   He won't be parted from it.

ARTY   *to the Captain* Don't take any notice.

KAY   It's one of those autograms, isn't it? From the Living History series.

14

ARTY   That's right. Twentieth Century Commando.

GUINEVER   It looks more like a Twenty-first Century Drunk.

ENID   What's the plan?

LANCE   We're going to play in the street.

ARTY   *What?!*

He jumps. **Captain Courage** *jumps, too.*

LANCE   You wanted to, didn't you? What d'you think, Beowulf? Now we've got this far . . .

BEOWULF   Better than hanging around here with Grandma Courage.

ARTY   *firmly*   Captain Courage is coming with us.

Captain Courage *falls over at this point.* **Guinever** *staggers about, laughing.*

GUINEVER   Captain Courage? *That?*

ARTY   He's all right when you know how to handle him.   *He sets the* **Captain** *on his feet*   There you are.

CAPTAIN COURAGE   Where *did* I leave my umbrella?

ENID   You what?

LANCE   We've got plenty of food. How about you?

KAY   We stopped off and got some stuff at British Home Stores. I told mum we were going down the levels, so she won't be expecting us back till tonight. I can give her a buzz from Level One.

LANCE   Won't she mind?

GUINEVER   Be too late to mind, won't it?

ARTY   Do they have telecoms on Level One?

KAY   We'll soon find out – well, sooner or later . . .

They set off down the stairs. **Lance, Beowulf** *and* **Kay** *are in a bunch behind* **Guinever.** **Enid** *hangs back and follows with* **Arty,** *looking back at* **Captain Courage,** *who is the last to leave. He draws his gun.*

CAPTAIN COURAGE   It's a very fine morning.

SCENE TWO

A landing on the stairs. A large sign reads: LEVEL TEN. Another sign reads: STAIRCASE TO LEVEL NINE OUT OF USE. DANGER MEN AT WORK. There are no men at work.

ARTY Might have guessed these'd be blocked.

CAPTAIN COURAGE Isn't it a nice day? If you get me the wool –

ALL EXCEPT ARTY Shuddup!

ARTY *to the Captain* You said that to *me*, didn't you?

CAPTAIN COURAGE What beautiful embroidery, my dear.

Arty looks thoughtful. The others have not noticed.

BEOWULF Which way shall we go, then? The West Stairs are the nearest, but they may be U.S. too.

LANCE Well, we might find an elevation unit. If we don't we'll just have to go on to the South Stairs.

GUINEVER So long as they're open. I bet *everything* on this level's out of order.

LANCE Tell you what, I reckon the planners that designed this place didn't want people going up and down between levels.

KAY Most people don't want to, anyway.

GUINEVER Only because it's so difficult.

KAY Who'd want to be on Level Ten if they didn't have to?

ARTY But we *are* on Level Ten.

CAPTAIN COURAGE *Who's* a pretty boy, then?

BEOWULF Look out for Level Tenners.

Beowulf, Kay and Guinever walk away.

ENID My mum would have a fit if she knew we were down here.

ARTY So'd mine.

ENID At this rate it'll take all day to get to the street.

ARTY Probably.

CAPTAIN COURAGE How are your cauliflowers coming along?

16

ENID He's a nutter.

ARTY He's all right.

CAPTAIN COURAGE Kitty–kitty–kitty . . .

ENDI I wish Guinever had brought her pocket video-viewer. If we don't get back by eight we'll miss *The Dark Age Saga*.

ARTY You'll have to catch up with the repeat tomorrow morning.

CAPTAIN COURAGE Kitty–kitty–kitty . . .

ENID *as they move away* It was brilliant last night. Did you see it?

Arty shakes his head. He is having problems with the control module.

ENID It was brilliant. There was this huge great wedding – well, there was going to be, with Guinever and Lancelot, 'cause you know Arthur divorced Guinever a couple of weeks ago, well, anyway, they were just getting married and she had this *fantastic* dress, you know, all . . . all, well, you know, and then Merlin rushes in and says the Vikings are coming. It ended there. There was all smoke rolling across the credits . . .

ARTY Come in, Captain, are you receiving me?

CAPTAIN COURAGE Kitty–kitty–kitty . . .

ENID My mum says she can remember when *The Dark Age Saga* began. She can remember when there wasn't any *Dark Age Saga*.

ARTY I wish there wasn't now. I wish it would finish. People might start calling their kids something different.

CAPTAIN COURAGE Kitty–kitty–kitty–kitty–kitty–kitty–kitty . . .

ARTY *hitting the control module* Everyone you meet's called Lancelot or Guinever or Kay or Merlin.

ENID And Enid.

CAPTAIN COURAGE Nice kitty. Come to Gran.

ARTY There's *five* Arthurs in my Fourth Year Horizontal Band Module. Not counting *me*.

CAPTAIN COURAGE Lovely weather for the time of year.

KAY *reappearing* Come on, you two. Suppose the Level Tenners get you?

He goes off. **Arty** *and* **Enid** *run after him in a panic.* **Captain Courage** *shambles after them.*

SCENE THREE

The Walkway, very dark and murky, near the head of the West Stairs. **Captain Courage** *has become rather indistinct.*

ENID I want to go back.

GUINEVER Shuddup.

ARTY Why's it so dark?

CAPTAIN COURAGE Isn't it a nice day?

LANCE It's the smoke.

ENID Smoke? Is there a fire? Quick –

GUINEVER Shuddup!

BEOWULF They don't use the central heating on Level Ten. They chop up their furniture and burn it. Everyone knows that. They aren't like us.

GUINEVER They keep their firewood in the bath.

BEOWULF Scroungers, my father says.

KAY They get behind with the rent, and that.

ARTY But they are *people* . . . aren't they?

CAPTAIN COURAGE What beautiful embroidery, my dear.

LANCE Can't you keep him quiet?

BEOWULF Sssh! What's that up ahead?

KAY Oh, just some old biddy. They do have Senior Citizens down here, you know.

GUINEVER Yeah . . . combat biddies . . .

ENID When can we eat? I'm starving. It's hours since we left home.

BEOWULF Soon as we get off Level Ten. Not long now.

GUINEVER If the stairs are open.

KAY Well, if they're not we'll just have to go on to the next flight.

ENID But that'll be another hour.

LANCE We aren't stopping to eat on Level Ten.

18

BEOWULF Hey! Sssh! Look there . . .

LANCE Where?

They all crowd together.

BEOWULF In the stairwell.

KAY Level Tenners.

ARTY Let's go back. Lance, let's go back.

CAPTAIN COURAGE Isn't it a nice day?

LANCE *Keep him quiet.*

ENID There's dozens of them.

KAY Trick of the light.

BEOWULF What light?

ENID They'll massacre us.

GUINEVER No, they won't. No one's massacring me.

ENID But we're not ready.

GUINEVER I'm always ready.

*The four big ones stand firm. **Enid** cowers behind **Guinever**. **Arty** manoeuvres **Captain Courage** into the darkness and lays a finger to his lips. The **Captain** smiles blankly and vanishes. Suddenly a **Level Tenner** appears in front of them.*

LEVEL TENNER 1 Who's that, then?

BEOWULF You what?

LEVEL TENNER 2 *advancing* Who's that? Who's there?

LANCE What?

LEVEL TENNERS *in the background –* They must come from upstairs.

         – Foreigners!

         – Don't even understand English.

         – Have them for breakfast . . .

LEVEL TENNER 1 *coming in close and counting* There's only six of them.

ARTY *whispering* Seven.

LEVEL TENNER 1 There's twenty-two of us.

LEVEL TENNER 2 By the time we've finished with you, you won't even match your computer records.

*The **Level Tenners** advance, a typical street gang, much older and bigger than the **Rose Street Gang**, and armed.*

LEVEL TENNER 1   Put your hands up.

*They obey. **Arty**, who is clasping the control module, raised only one hand. The **Level Tenners** close in.*

LEVEL TENNER 2   *counting laboriously*   One, two . . . three, four . . . five, six . . . seven, eight . . . nine, ten . . . eleven . . . Here, one of you only got one arm?

***Arty** looks toward **Captain Courage**, nods and pounces on the control module. The **Captain**'s arm, with gun, emerges from the murk.*

LEVEL TENNER 2   Twelve! Whaaaaaa?

*The rest of **Captain Courage** advances, prancing and swivelling, towards the **Level Tenners**, who break ground.*

ARTY   Now!

CAPTAIN COURAGE   People like you ought to be locked up!

*Gun at the ready, he chivvies the **Level Tenners** into line. They begin to retreat.*

LEVEL TENNERS   It's a ghost.

　　　　　　　　　　　　　－It's one of *them* . . .

　　　　　　　　　　　　　－A zombie . . .

　　　　　　　　　　　　　－From outer space, like . . .

ARTY   Go on!

CAPTAIN COURAGE   *at full volume*   Here! Kitty–kitty–kitty–kitty–kitty . . .

*The **Level Tenners** retreat in disorder. **Captain Courage** pursues them.*

ARTY   Get them, Captain!

CAPTAIN COURAGE   How are your cauliflowers coming along?

*The **Level Tenners** run for it, with the **Rose Street Gang** in jeering pursuit. **Arty** stays put, operating the module. **Captain Courage** comes back.*

ARTY   I don't suppose they've ever seen an autogram before. Good thing you came with us, eh?

CAPTAIN COURAGE   If you get me the wool I'll knit one for you.

SCENE FOUR

*The Gang have bivouacked in a 'garden' for the night. A sign reads: LEVEL FIVE: HYDROPONIC LEISURE FACILITY: LOWER NORTH WALKWAY. They are eating, drinking and toasting **Arty. Arty**, modest, toasts **Captain Courage**, who is hanging about.*

LANCE   Right, now, we'll rest up here, and tomorrow we'll go on down to the street.

ENID   What did your mum say when you told her you wouldn't be back tonight?

LANCE   Not much she could say, was there? She knows how long it takes to get down the levels.

ARTY   King Arthur lives on one level.

CAPTAIN COURAGE   *softly*   Kitty–kitty–kitty . . .

BEOWULF   What?

ARTY   In *The Dark Age Saga* he lives on the ground. They all do. Even the castles only go up a little way.

GUINEVER   You don't wish you lived in the Dark Ages, do you? What about all those Danes and Vikings?

ARTY   They aren't in it every week.

CAPTAIN COURAGE   If you get me the wool . . .

KAY   Danes and Vikings aren't any worse than Level Tenners.

ARTY   Must be nice, though, to go out of doors whenever you feel like it. And live near the sea.

ENID   The Vikings come out of the sea.

BEOWULF   Not all the time. Anyway, sometimes it's Picts and Saxons. It isn't always Vikings.

LANCE   Anyway, King Arthur always wins . . . in the end.

ARTY   Who needs King Arthur? We've got Captain Courage.

CAPTAIN COURAGE   What beautieautieautieautoooo-woooooooooowoooolooool . . .

LANCE   *doubtfully*   I don't think we'll have him much longer. He doesn't look very well.

CAPTAIN COURAGE   . . . ooolooooowooool . . .

GUINEVER   I wish you could stop him talking.

ARTY   He only talks when I do.

CAPTAIN COURAGE   Whaaaaaaat booooootifyfyfyfy my dear. Dear. Dear.

BEWULF   *jealously*   Well, *you* stop talking, then. He wasn't this bad when I had him.

LANCE   Let's get some sleep. Tomorrow's a long day. We've got to get down to the street and back again.

ARTY   Captain Courage will stand guard, won't you, Captain?

CAPTAIN COURAGE   *Who's* a pretty boy, then?

ENID   Our auntie got like that. She had to be put away . . .

ARTY   We aren't putting the Captain away.

CAPTAIN COURAGE   Where *did* I leave . . . my . . . where *did* I . . . where *did* I . . .

LANCE   Of course not. But I wish we could switch him off.   *Arty snorts*   Sometimes.

SCENE FIVE

*Daylight, out of doors. On a wall a rusty sign reads ROSE STREET. From a dark doorway the **Gang** come out, followed by **Captain Courage**, now in a critical condition.*

ENID   Coo, isn't it *bright*? Where's it coming from?

GUINEVER   What?

ENID   The light.

BEOWULF   That's daylight, thicko. The sun.

KAY   Smells funny, doesn't it?

LANCE   That's just fresh air.

ENID   What are all those funny things like big boxes?

BEOWULF   Don't you know anything?

GUINEVER   You shut up, Beowulf Hopkins. She hasn't been out in the street for years. Bet you haven't, neither.

ENID   Well, what are they?

LANCE   Houses.

KAY   What people used to live in, years ago . . . like King Arthur.

22

ENID One *each?*

ARTY What are all those little square holes?

LANCE I dunno. Winters, or something.

BEOWULF Windows. Dad's thinking of cutting one in our wall if he can get planning permission.

KAY King Arthur's got windows, hasn't he? Fancy not knowing that.

ARTY His come to a point, though.

CAPTAIN COURAGE *very faint* Here, kitty–kitty–kitty . . .

GUINEVER Well, here we are. This is it. Rose Street. What are we waiting for? Let's play.

LANCE I reckon we've got an hour, then we'd better start back, if we want to be home for dinner.

They scatter. **Arty** *and the* **Captain** *remain.*

KAY *going* Let's get into two teams – Beowulf, you pick for your side . . .

LANCE Leave that module, Arty. We don't need Captain Courage along. He'll muck up the numbers.

ARTY They don't want you any more.

CAPTAIN COURAGE *thinly* If you get me the woo . . . oo . . . oo . . . ool . . .

ARTY You should have died a glorious death in battle – with the Level Tenners.

CAPTAIN COURAGE . . . umbrella . . .

ARTY Covered with honour.

CAPTAIN COURAGE . . . cauliflowers . . .

ARTY Well, I know what you were really like; a great leader.

CAPTAIN COURAGE Kitty . . . kitty . . .

ARTY This won't hurt . . . it'll be very quick . . .

Arty *puts the control module on the ground and grinds it under his heel. He turns to face the* **Captain** *and salutes.*

ARTY Goodbye, Captain.

Captain Courage *writhes and vanishes.*

CAPTAIN COURAGE *a disembodied voice* Isn't it a nice day?

ARTY *sorrowfully* He was a very gallant gentleman.

LANCE *yelling from the distance* Come on! It was you that wanted to play in the street!

ARTY Coming! *he lingers, looking up at the street sign* I wonder, what's a rose?

STAGING THE PLAY

Setting

The action uses many locations in the Rose Street Development, so the main floor of the school hall will be a more flexible performance area than a proscenium stage. Keep the layout simple. Don't be tempted to build the sort of furniture sets you sometimes see on television. They are difficult to make and rarely look effective.

If you set the play 'in the round', you will be able to place some of the acting areas among the audience. You will also be able to use the central area for the walkways, the Hydroponic Memorial Facility and Garden. If possible, put extra walkways around the back – they will help the actors to move from one area to another without disturbing the drama.

The acting areas among the audience should be raised a little, but the action in the central area will work best on ground level. A simple method of marking out the walkways is to stick lines of white PVC tape on the floor. You may find it visually effective to link the walkways to the 'interior' areas by running white tape around the edges of the raised acting platforms.

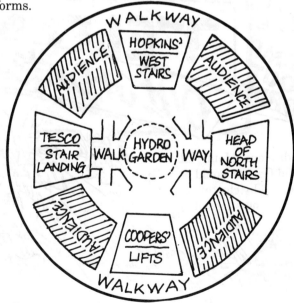

Signs are an important feature of the play. Think carefully about how they should look – futuristic and yet shabby. The signs will change as the gang moves down through the levels. This will help to mark the stages of the Gang's progress to the street.

The Hydroponic Memorial Facility and Garden could be represented by clusters of potted plants and strips of plastic grass.

Characters

The characters in the Rose Street gang have their own personalities. Pay special attention to the way each character speaks and moves and how he/she reacts to other members of the gang. Make sure these character differences don't get 'lost' during the play itself.

Captain Courage

Much of the play's dramatic effect will depend on the way Captain Courage is played. In the way he looks, speaks and moves, he should have a special presence on stage – the audience should really notice him.

Dress

If you put him in an Arctic commando outfit instead of the standard camouflage kit, you could highlight him with two follow-spots (with steel blue filters). This should give him a ghostly luminous effect. Boots, rifle, gloves will all add to the macho male hero image. For the face, try using a half-mask blended to the mouth and chin with stage make-up.

Voice

If Captain Courage is played by a girl, it will be easier to create the voice of a nineteenth-century granny. The sound of the voice should be a complete contrast to the character's physical image. Captain Courage uses only a limited number of phrases and, being a machine, he says each phrase in exactly the same way every time. In rehearsal, find the 'tune' for each phrase, memorise it, and then stick to it.

Movement

As Arty points out, Captain Courage has been programmed with only a few simple moves. Like the voice, they never vary. Make them larger than life and perform each action with a clear start and stop. Exploit the absurd contrasts between his voice and movements. These, more than anything else, give the character his special appeal.

Captain Courage moves only if (a) the control module moves or, (b) he gets an electronic or voice signal from his operator. Arty becomes very skilled with the control module, and by the end of the play Captain Courage has moments when he seems almost human. Give plenty of time in rehearsal to developing this 'electronic' relationship between Arty and Captain Courage.

27

Sound

There are lots of machines in the play, and they all make noises – Factcentre, entryphone, Captain Courage's command module and, possibly, speakers in the walkways playing background music. The sounds should add to the dramatic effect and they could also help to establish a sense of the future. But be careful not to overdo them. Experiment with the clicks, bleeps and tunes that can be made on portable synthesizers. Remember that sound made offstage to specific actions onstage should be properly co-ordinated. This applies particularly to the Factcentre, which uses four voices as well as electronic sound.

You could heighten the feeling of bright open space in the final scene by fading in the faint sound of birdsong in the distance.

Lighting

You could either use general light, or light each area separately. There are two moments in the play which call for special lighting effects:

1 The appearance of the Level Tenners. One possibility here is to use dim shafts of lights through smoke. The Level Tenners would then appear in silhouette. (You can buy stage smoke in aerosol canisters. The sound of spraying the smoke in the dark will add to the menacing atmosphere.)

2 The gang's emergence into daylight. Keep some lighting power in reserve to create the change from interior light to sunshine.

ACTIVITIES ON AND AROUND THE PLAY

Drama work

1a Imagine that on Level Eleven there is a special unit called 'Rose Street – Past and Present'. The unit contains photographs (or holograms) showing aspects of life before the Rose Street Development. Alongside are photographs of life after the Development was built. The exhibition is a celebration of progress. It has several sections:

Health and Safety	**Education**
Transport	**Family**
Old People	**Leisure**
Pollution	**Shopping**
Energy	

Divide into groups of four, each group working on one of the above sections. Or a group could invent its own section. Create two tableaux ('frozen' pictures) to look like photographs of Rose Street which show the contrast between the past and present. Give each tableau a 'caption'.

b Take it in turns to show each set of tableaux to the class. Allow time for questions and comments from the class about the aspect of life you have chosen to depict.

2a Not all the members of the Rose Street Gang feel the same about life on Level Eleven. Skim through the play to find what Arty, Beowulf, Guinever and Enid think of it. Work in groups of four and role-play the four characters. In turn, put Arty, Beowulf, Guinever and Enid in the 'hot seat'. The rest of the group should ask questions to draw out each character's attitudes towards life in the Rose Street Development.

b Then, still in character, tell your version of the journey to Rose Street to the rest of the group. For example, how would Enid's story of the journey differ from Arty's?

3a Still in groups of four, call back from the past two members of the planning committee responsible for the building of Rose Street Development. Let them describe their plans and expectations of the building.

b The other two people from the group should role-play a couple of local media reporters. Ask the planners how far the building has fulfilled their expectations. Are there any design changes they would make in the light of experience?

4a What does the inside of a housing unit in the Development look like? We know that each one has a Factcentre, a living area and a utility area. Also, somehow, Arty, Lance and Beowulf seem to be always under their mothers' feet. Skim through the play to find other information about the units. Then draw some plans to show a possible layout of a housing unit. Include sketches which give an impression of what it is like to live in it.

b Work in groups of four. One person, an estate agent, shows the other three (a family group) round a housing unit that is for sale. The estate agent points out with pride all its special features. However, some of the machinery unexpectedly begins to go wrong. How does the estate agent cope?

5a The Hopkins family are hoping to get planning permission to install a window in their unit. What other features of houses or flats today might appeal to the Hopkinses' sense of style? Remember, they seem to like 'old-fashioned' things. List three or four changes they might want to make.

b Imagine that the Hopkinses have made all the planned changes to their housing unit. They have invited the Cooper family to tea, mainly to show off their achievements. Work in groups of four to role-play the adults. Imagine the conversation between the snooty Hopkinses and the critical Coopers. Begin the scene at the point when the Cooper family announce their arrival on the entryphone.

6a Arty asks a lot of what seem to us very simple questions. Make a list of all the things he would like to know about that we find very familiar.

b Work with a partner. Arty is helping a senior citizen move to another housing unit. People of Level Eleven probably throw everything away when they move, but this old person wants to hang on to some very 'curious' objects (e.g. a flower vase, a walking stick, a picture of a family holiday by the sea, etc.). Imagine that the old person remembers how these objects were used. Role-play a conversation between Arty and the old person in which the objects are the starting-points for stories about life before the Rose Street Development.

7a We hear more about the Level Tenners than we actually see of them. What sort of things are said about them? Look again through the play and make a list.

b Imagine that, for a dare, Guinever has been sent to spy on the Level Tenners. She has sneaked down the stairs and has found a crack in the concrete through which she can watch without being seen. Work in a small group. Decide what Guinever can see through the crack. Then one of you, in the character of Guinever, should recount her story to the gang. Would Guinever tell the bare facts, or would she exaggerate?

8 Stories and rumours alter in the telling. Try this exercise in groups of five. After the trip to Level Ten, a member of the Rose Street Gang visits another group and tells them about the trip keeping it as exciting and interesting as possible. Someone else now takes up the same story and passes it on to another group. In this way the story goes around the groups, with a new teller each time, until it returns to its original group. (About five tellings should be enough.) At the end, has the picture of the Level Tenners been changed in any way?
    You could keep *different* stories going around the groups at the same time.

9 We learn a lot about events on Level Ten, but what about the other levels? Work in groups of five or six. Imagine the Rose Street Gang stopped at another level on their way to the street. What if they came across a level that was completely but recently deserted, or one that was sealed off (with warning signs to possible intruders), or a friendly level where most things work? Plan and act out a short role-play for the class.

10 The parents don't seem to be worried about any dangers their children may come across on the trip to the street. Suppose that, on the return journey, Enid got lost. How would the parents react then? Work in groups of six. Make up and act a scene to show what the parents feel after the Gang's return to Level Eleven without Enid.

11 The play ends soon after the Gang comes out into daylight in Rose Street. But this moment could also be the start of a new story about the Gang's adventures in the street and beyond. The story could show the changes in their attitudes and their relationships with people who live 'on the ground' in houses. You might decide that the Gang like the street and want to visit it regularly, or that they hate it and prefer their safe lifestyle on Level Ten. Plan a sequel either in story or play form. Let it start with Arty looking at the sign and asking 'What's a rose?'.

Writing
1 The local newspaper did a big feature on the Rose Street Development when it was officially opened. Write the headline and the report that appeared in the newspaper. Try to describe what happened that day, how things looked and sounded to you. In your report, include opinions from people living nearby and from important personages, like the mayor.

2 Write a short article for Arty's local paper. The article could be about an aspect of life in the Development, or a recent event that took place on Level Eleven. It could be funny or serious.

3 How is Arty's day structured? He has no sun to wake him up or night to put him to sleep, so how is time organised? Does his family have official meal times? When is he expected to attend the Education centre?
Write about a day in the life of Arty Cooper. This could be in the form of a diary entry. Each insert could be written against a time in the 'day'. As it is a private diary, Arty could include some of his own personal comments on people and events.

4 If you could leave a time capsule (a box of present-day objects) for the Rose Street Gang, what would you put in it? Work in small groups. Make a list of ten things which will show the Gang what your life today is like. Write a set of explanations that the Gang will read as the objects are taken out of the capsule in the twenty-first century.

5   Imagine yourself as Arty standing in the street after the long journey down through the levels. What can you see, hear, smell and touch that is strange and new? Write down your thoughts and feelings as they occur to you.

6   You are still Arty. The rest of the gang has returned to the Development, but you have stayed behind to see night fall. Describe your feelings as, for the first time in your life, you watch the approach of darkness and the night sky fill with stars.

7   Suppose *you* had to live in the Rose Street Development for a time. How would not having any contact with the outside world change your life? Make a list of the experiences you would miss most. Choose one that you feel particularly strongly about and say why you would miss it so much.

8   Now leap forward in time by about 100 years. Imagine that people no longer live in the Rose Street Development. The building itself has been preserved as an example of twenty-first-century architecture, almost like a museum. By the main door there is a plaque or board bearing an inscription to be read by visitors to the building. The aim is to make visitors think about what the Development once was. Write the inscription on the plaque.

PEOPLE AND SPACES

Tower blocks

Rose Street Development is a building of the future, a massive tower block. It protects people from the outside world – from the wind and rain, but also from fresh air and sunshine.

Over fifty years ago, Le Corbusier (a French-Swiss architect) designed a high-rise city of concrete tower blocks set in parkland. He wanted people to enjoy the green spaces for sports and games. Flats in the blocks would be connected by long corridors like 'streets in the air'. Le Corbusier wanted each flat to get lots of sunlight and have a beautiful view. All this could be done cheaply by making the tower blocks tall, and by building them from mass-produced parts.

The city was never built, but Le Corbusier's ideas were taken up by many architects and planners all over the world. High-rise buildings can be seen in many cities. They were popular with local councils and town planners for many years.

1 Think about the good and bad aspects of tower blocks. Use the resources on these pages to help you. Jot your ideas on a piece of paper, and then have a 'brainstorming' session in class. List the possible advantages and disadvantages on the board until you have a good selection of ideas. It may help if you put a time-limit of, say, fifteen minutes on the 'brainstorming' session.

BENEFITS of the TOWER BLOCK
USES LESS LAND
GOVERNMENT GRANTS
FOR BLOCKS OVER 6
STOREYS, CHEAPER TO
BUILD, QUICKER TO
BUILD, CHEAPER TO
MAINTAIN and so
LOWER RENTS

TOWN PLANNING DEPARTMENT

In Corbusier's vision tower blocks were friendly, pleasant places to live. Apartments would be noise-free; the long corridors which provided access to them would form 'streets in the air'. Elevators would give easy access to all floors and to the roof gardens at the top of each block.

2 A town council has arranged a meeting for people who are going to be moved into a new tower block in a few months. Choose five or six people to speak about the problems they think they will have living in the tower block. Choose two council representatives to answer their questions. Hold the meeting, and make sure no one speaks for too long.

3 Imagine you have moved into the new tower block. What do you think of it so far? Decide whether or not the council has kept its promises. Write a letter to your council representative to complain about the conditions or congratulate him/her on a good job.

4 Work in groups of five or six. The local newspaper wants to print a feature story about life in the city's tower blocks. The paper is keen to show as wide a range of opinions as possible. Choose one person to be the reporter – he or she should prepare a short list of questions to ask. The other people should choose roles to represent people who live in the tower block and have strong views on it.

Hold the interview, making sure you stay in character. Record it on tape if possible.

Now change roles so that you all share in writing up the newspaper story and producing some pictures for it. Keep referring back to the interview. What headline will you have for your story?

Compare your newspaper features in class. What do they have in common? Do they make any important points?

5 The new tower block has raised some important questions about the council's housing policy. A television company wants to hold a studio debate about it. There will be a panel of experts to answer questions from the audience, and the audience will be made up of the tower block's residents. The debate should be chaired by someone who is not biased (perhaps by your teacher).

The panel of experts could include:
– the editor or reporter from your local paper
– the caretaker or maintenance supervisor of the tower block
– a representative from the council
– the architect who designed the tower block
– a social worker

Prepare some questions for the panel. Decide on what topic each 'expert' can be expected to give answers.

If your debate comes to any conclusions, write these up on the board.

SMALL BUDGET FOR HOUSING IN AREA... LONG WAITING LISTS... PRIORITIES...TIME... MONEY FOR REPAIRS... INCREASES IN RATES... POLITICS IN COUNCIL...

ATTITUDE OF RESIDENTS...BUREAUCRACY IN COUNCIL...QUALITY OF BUILDING WORK... CHILDREN ON ESTATE... AVAILABILITY OF STAFF, MONEY & TIME FOR REPAIRS

LE CORBUSIER'S IDEAL DESIGN...SPACE, LIGHT, MODERN CONCEPT... FOLLOWING BRIEF GIVEN BY COUNCIL...CUTBACKS... BUILDING MATERIALS... PRESSURE OF TIME & MONEY...PEOPLE CHANGING THEIR MINDS

EDITOR WEEKLY RAG   CARETAKER   COUNCIL REPRESENTATIVE   ARCHITECT   SOCIAL WORKER

HISTORY OF AREA... CHANGES IN HOUSING... LETTERS FROM READERS... 'WEEKLY RAG' INVESTIGATES & CAMPAIGNS...DO ARCHITECTS' IDEAS WORK IN PRACTICE? WHO'S RESPONSIBLE?

WHAT ABOUT THE LIFTS?

THE COUNCIL'S POLICY TOWARDS OLD PEOPLE...

MY CASELOAD...PROBLEMS OF LIFE IN TOWER BLOCKS —ISOLATION, ALIENATION, CRIME...DESTRUCTION OF ENVIRONMENT... PLANNERS...PLAYSPACE FOR CHILDREN... REHOUSING FOR FAMILIES...WHO'S RESPONSIBLE?

37

A housing estate in the north of England

Identity

Our territory

1 Write down the thoughts that come to the mother's mind as she walks with her baby along the pavement.

2 Imagine the baby can see with an adult's eyes and think with an adult's mind. What does the baby think about his/her own future in this environment? Shape the baby's thoughts into a poem.

The environment we live in affects the way we feel about ourselves. It affects our identity. Arty and his friends have lived in the Rose Street Development all their lives, but they have not yet found their own separate identity as individuals or as a gang.

Take a look at yourself in your own environemnt. Begin with your own home, your *family territory*.

– Is it a house or a flat?

– How long have you lived there?

– What makes your home different from those of your neighbours?

Inside your home you probably have your own *personal territory*.

– Do you have any special pictures or objects that help to define it as your space?

– Do you like to keep it tidy or untidy?

Outside your home you live in a *neighbourhood territory*.

– What are its distinctive sights, sounds and smells?

– Do you know any stories that are associated with your neighbourhood?

– Does your neighbourhood feel *right* to you? There must be places that make you feel uneasy, out of place. What is there that makes you feel out of place?

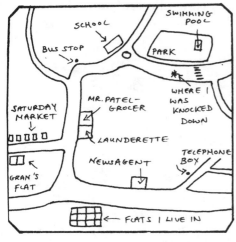

3 Draw a simple map of your own personal neighbourhood. Include details that you will not find on an official map. Mark where important things have happened, your favourite shops, people, meeting places, play areas, etc.

What is distinctive about your neighbourhood territory?

Our territories are also shaped by our relationships with people. We usually try to make friends with people who feel the same way as we do about things.

– Look at different groups, young and old, in your neighbourhood. What interests do they have in common? How do they show their common interests? Do they dress in a special way, talk or behave in a particular manner? Think of some examples of both younger and older groups in your area.

These territories make us feel secure and confident in places and relationships. They help to give us a sense of our own identity.

But what about the world outside?
The world outside our territories can be unfamiliar,
challenging and unpredictable. It may not feel *right* to us. But
if we can express our identity only within our familiar
territories, how will we get on in the world outside?
– What sort of
people seem to be
good at coping with
new places and
relationships?

4   Compile a
personal identity kit.
This could include
– photographs of
yourself and family
– the map of your
territories
– comments on your
territories (what you
like about them,
how you think they
could be improved)

– cuttings from your local paper referring to people and places
you know
– a description of a person who has been a strong influence on
you.

5   Telling stories can be a useful way of getting to know
ourselves. In groups of four or five, set up a story exchange.
Each person in the group tells a story associated with his or
her territories. This may be a personal experience, or a recent
event, or a popular local story such as a place being haunted.
Include lots of detail in the stories, and try to tell them in a
way that keeps the listeners wanting to know more.

The Level Tenners
6   Arty says that the Level Tenners have identity. In the
confrontation on Level Ten we learn a lot about the strengths
and weaknesses of each group. Look again at Scene Three in
Act Two, and then read the following description of the Level
Tenners from the short story by Jan Mark from which the
play was adapted.*

40

The Level Tenners were a menacing myth rather than a dangerous reality. No one knew very much about them and what was unknown was invented, such as their numbers, reputedly around fifteen – or fifty. For a start they went to a different Education Centre, on their own level (the Rose Street Gang were passing it now) and they came from the kind of families that the Coopers and Hopkinses and even the Lamberts would never associate with, even if the planners had encouraged upward mobility, or downward. Level Ten was a problem floor. On to it were shelved all the tenants who could not or would not pay rent and who, as rumour had it, unscrewed their doors and used them as tables, chopped up their tables for firewood and kept the firewood in the bath. Level Ten dwellings were no more provided with grates and chimneys than were those on the other twelve levels, but the tenants constructed flues out of cans welded end to end and a sooty fog drifted along the walkways and landings at two metres above the floor.

The Level Tenners began to issue like dark fumes from the stairwell. On they came. Even Lance and Guinever retreated slightly, and the others flattened themselves against the wall. Arty looked at the Level Tenners.

They wore armour-plated trousers and rivet-studded tunics and steel-capped boots; one or two had horned helmets. All were armed with blunt instruments and sharp ones. They reminded Arty a little of Captain Courage, not as he actually was but as he had appeared on the package, only Captain Courage had had the lean fitness of a man who was trained for action and fed on red meat. The Level Tenners were lean with the scrawniness of those who trained for action on Spicy Nibbles and Coolacola. In spite of their numbers, Arty knew they had certain disadvantages. They kept firewood in the bath, it was well known. They might have telecom and Network Video, if they didn't smash them up, but the chances of their ever having seen a hologram were remote. Certainly they would never have seen an autogram.

Jan Mark

a Do you think that Arty is right about the Level Tenners – that they have identity?

b How do you think the Level Tenners feel about their territories? Would they ever go down to the street?

c Are the Level Tenners stronger or weaker than the Rose Street Gang? In what ways?

7 Work in groups of six. Create a tableau (a 'frozen' picture) representing the 'menacing myth' of the Level Tenners. Then add captions or phrases that express the reality behind the myth. These could include thoughts they have about home, people on other floors, the authorities, the Education Centre.

8 In the same groups, improvise a scene in which a group of Level Tenners describe the Captain Courage incident to some of their gang who were not there. What sort of plans might they make for future confrontations with the Rose Street Gang?

9 The meeting of the two gangs on Level Ten is a visually powerful scene. Its drama depends not only on what is happening on the surface, but on the feelings hidden beneath it.

Television is an exciting medium, because it can create visual images and also convey feelings that lie *behind* the images. If you can get hold of a video camera, use it to explore the dramatic qualities of the scene. Don't attempt a TV adaption, but use the camera to compose pictures, some distant, some close-up, which draw out the tension between the two levels of the drama. You could then select your best shots and organise them into a dramatic sequence on paper (see the pictures below for ideas).

Level Tenners appear through the smoke 6 secs

Enid's eyes 1 sec

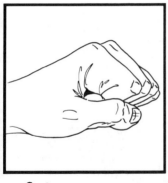

Guinever's fist
clenching 2 secs

Level Tenners move
forward 3 secs

New City

Here is an extract from a story about a city which, like the
Rose Street Development, exists in the early twenty-first
century.

New City glittered under its steel-and-Plexiglas dome,
eternally air-conditioned, forever beyond the reach of
rain, snow or frost. Its lighting system provided for the
same amount of illumination daily whether the sun
shone or not. However, there was provision agreed on by
the Council for certain gray days, as it had been found
that continual, unfluctuating light created monotony and
affected people's mental states. The dome was
soundproof too, so that the constant air traffic overhead
made only the thinnest hum. Once a supersonic
transport had wandered off its wilderness flyway and
had created a sonic boom of such proportions that almost
a quarter of the dome had cracked, and a dozen
unprotected houses in Old City had been reduced to
rubble. However, that had been a rare accident: the SSTs
and the Global Freight Ships ordinarily flew only
specified wilderness and ocean routes between the widely
scattered population centres.

The people in New City marveled that anyone in his
right mind would live outside its protective dome. Only
eccentrics or the very poor clung to the unsheltered
slopes, and each year the number of those decreased so
that the growing population within the dome was
intense. There was talk about the need to enlarge the
canopy by another hundred square miles.

Of the Nature Squad, only Fay lived outside the dome, not far from Aunt Zeb's house. Her envy of Patrick, Lester and Sylvie was keen. During the school year she went regularly to New City to school, and each day when she had to board the Turbo-van that took her and other Old City children back to their homes, she felt humiliated. Outwardly, she pretended that she much preferred life under the open sky.

'My mother and father love the wind and the rain,' she would declare with desperate boldness to questioning classmates. 'And so do I; I'd hate to live all bottled up, without ever hearing the wind or anything.'

That part of it was true. Aside from the dome's prestige, and its protection from sonic booms, lightning, and disease germs, she did prefer the natural sound of wind or rain, and the real sun on her skin. But it was not true that her parents lived where they did out of choice. It was simply that they were too poor to live elsewhere.

Adrien Stoutenburg, *Out There*, Bodley Head

1 Imagine that it is ten years since New City was built, together with its dome. The council has just decided to mark this anniversary by giving each family a souvenir magazine. The magazine will have pictures showing the good aspects of life inside the dome. It will cover topics such as:

– health of the citizens
– control over the weather
– quality of the shops
– facilities for sports and other leisure activities
– social life of the citizens.

Work in groups of four or five. Think about the benefits of life under the dome, then draw some preparatory sketches for the magazine. Use a roll of paper or some transparencies for an overhead projector. Group your sketches into a sequence or into the topics listed above. Then add a commentary, either written, or spoken and recorded on a cassette. Think carefully how the commentary will affect the 'message' presented by the magazine.

2 In the story, Fay feels humiliated when she leaves the dome each day. What things in school might deepen her humiliation? Work in pairs or small groups. Explore some of the more subtle ways in which this could happen.

3 If Patrick, Lester and Sylvie have never been outside the dome, what do they think of the people who live on the slopes? Imagine that one of their classmates, who lives in the dome, has fallen ill. A rumour is running round the school that Fay brought in a virus from outside. How would they talk among themselves about it? Would they say anything to their teacher, or to Fay? Role-play their conversation.

4 Work with a partner. It is winter and the slopes are covered with a beautiful layer of snow. Fay wants to share her excitement with a friend. How might she persuade Sylvie to spend a day with her outside?

5 Suppose Sylvie is allowed to go outside with Fay. How does she describe her experience in the snow to a friend inside the dome? Still with your partner, act out their conversation.

Writing

6 Write down the thoughts that come into Fay's mind as she walks from the Turbo-van to her home after school one day.

7 As Fay's parents, write a letter to the Council applying for a home inside the dome.

8 Imagine that very fine cracks have been discovered in the dome's Plexiglas. The whole structure must be replaced. It will take two years to build a new dome, and during this time the New City will be exposed to the air and weather.

Write a radio broadcast in which the Council informs the dome's citizens what is about to happen. Bear in mind that the shock of this news could cause a panic reaction. Your broadcast will have to be carefully worded.

9 Write a story about the events which follow the radio broadcast.

10 Divide into groups of five or six. Read your stories to each other. Choose one of the stories to use as the basis for a radio play.

Sound can be a strong stimulus to the imagination. Creating an imaginary world of the future can be easier on radio than in the theatre. On the radio, you can use sounds to suggest environments, and radio can enter the minds of characters and 'hear' their thoughts. The setting of New City lends itself to interpretation through sound. Think how the sound inside the controlled world of the dome would contrast with the sounds of Old City exposed to nature. Experiment with recording various sounds for your play, and judge their effect on playback. Practise blending sounds with dialogue. Don't be afraid to throw out sounds that don't work.

A note about plot – to feel the drama of events after the dome cracks, the listeners will need to know something about events that happened before that. When writing your script, you may need to backtrack from the point where your story starts. Look again at the improvisations and writing you have done about New City: they could well come in useful here.

PEOPLE AND TECHNOLOGY

A telescreen in every home

Within the next few years, if current plans go ahead, most town dwellers will be able to have more than twenty international, national and local television channels piped into their homes. Following this could come a hundred or more computer services, eg:

1 Holidays and travel

You may be able to order promotion videos, book trains, flights and hotel rooms (and pay for them electronically by credit-card code) from your home/ computer/video terminal.

2 Bargain searches

You may be able to tell the computer to put on the screen the best buys at the local shops.

3 Political meetings

You may be able to let politicians know what you think by pressing a button or sending a longer electronic message.

EDUCATION
Lectures transmitted from local and national studios
Questions and discussion with other 'class' members through talk-back facility
Joint classes with foreign schools and universities
Dial-an-expert service – DIY, Cooking, Maths, French

MAIL
Letters sent and received instantly through printer
Message dialogues

INFORMATION
Weather forecast
Stock Exchange
What's on – hometown and major cities

MONEY
Bank statements
Tax return preparation
Personal accounting and direct payment of bills

SPECIAL SEARCHES
Best buys in local shops
Jobs
Houses

LIBRARY
Direct access to books and documents in local and foreign libraries
Encyclopedia Service

POLITICS
Attendance at political meetings from home
Questions through talkback facility

VIDEO-PHONE
Telephone with picture
Link with more than one person – coffee break chat or club committee meeting

Speakers
Camera
Microphones
Screen
Keyboard
Printer

SHOPPING
Mail order catalogue – ordering and payment
Weekly order to local supermarket
Travel Agents – video presentations of holidays on request

ENTERTAINMENT
TV – many local and international channels
Games with direct video link to players in other countries
Dial-a-film/video service
Live performances of music and theatre around the world
7-foot screen for those who can afford it

WORK AT HOME
Work documents received through printer
Video-linked 'face to face' business conferences
Direct access to company files
Link to secretaries

NEWSPAPERS
Fed directly through printer
Scan facility for items of personal interest
Foreign news broadcasts with English sub-titles

Eventually it will be possible to transmit pictures and speech from a home computer/video. The home computer/video will change the way we organise work, education and leisure. (Look at p. 48.)

1 How does the advertisement below try to make us buy the product? Look at its language and visual images. What are the advertisers trying to put across?

Now Technics lets you take control of an audio/video empire.

At last. Video good enough for Technics audio. Integrated into one remarkable audio/video system of astonishing capabilities and breathtaking performance.

It's a Technics 26-inch (measured diagonally) color TV monitor/receiver. A Technics VHS Hi-Fi video cassette recorder. An AM/FM stereo tuner/pre-amp with stereo TV sound.* Power amplifier. Linear tracking turntable. Auto-reverse cassette deck. A pair of three-way speakers. Even an optional compact disc player.

Its unified wireless remote lets you control this technological empire from across the room. The remote has its own LCD readout to show you precisely what function you've selected. So you can create an audio experience. A video experience. Or a blending of the two.

It's the audio/video empire that puts you in complete control. The experience is unforgettable. The name is Technics.

Technics
The science of sound

2   The style and technology of this type of product soon go out of date. Try to imagine what the next model might look like and the new features it will offer. How could it make the model in the advertisement seem old-fashioned?

Design an advertisement for the new model, taking special care over its language and visual images.

3a   Television in the future could still be used to show programmes that help us 'escape into another world'. For instance, the Dark Age Saga is very popular with the inhabitants of the Rose Street Development. The characters and setting of the saga have little to do with their lives, yet everybody is 'hooked' on it. Why? Suggest a few reasons.

b   We have our own 'sagas' too – *EastEnders*, *Dynasty*, *Coronation Street*, *Dallas*, *Brookside* and so on. Why do we get hooked on them? Which are the most popular TV serials in your class? Do a quick mini-survey by asking the class to put up their hands if they watch particular serials.

4   Work in groups of five or six. You have been employed by a TV company to devise a new serial that will be popular with viewers of your age.

a   Begin by doing some market research in your class.
– Should the serial be set in the past, present, or future?
– What types of characters do most of you prefer – people from real life, or figures from legends or science fiction?
– What type of plot should it have – how much adventure, glamour, 'human interest' situations?

b   Create a setting and characters for a story based on the responses you have found.

c   Write the story-line for the opening episode of the serial. Remember, you will need to create enough suspense to make the viewers want to watch the second episode.

d   Prepare the opening few minutes of the programme for presentation to the TV company (your teacher could perhaps work in the role as a representative of the company).

5   Alternatively, you could do a send-up of a TV saga. In your groups, you could create an extract of a saga to end all sagas – the ultimate in escapist fantasy using characters from well-known serials.

6 You are captain of the starship Seeker which ferries emigrants from Earth to fertile planets in other parts of the universe. Seeker has lost power and requires new fuel elements. These can be obtained only on the planet Dalma, the most hostile planet in the Galuvian galaxy. Your mission is to make an undetected landing.

Invent a video game using this cover description as your starting point.

7 How many hours television do you watch each week? Make a survey of your television viewing habits.

a Keep a record of your viewing during a typical week. Record the exact times you start and stop watching and the programmes you enjoyed most. Be careful not to change the normal pattern of your viewing during the survey. Remember to include

– breakfast television
– programmes on video recorders
– hired videos
– computer games.

b Compare your total of viewing hours with other people in the class. Work out the class's average.

The national average for young people aged 5–14 is 25 hours a week – over 3½ hours a day. In the future, people will have more free time to watch television. What, do you think, is a reasonable number of hours for a person to sit in front of a television or video screen each week? Why do you think this?

Computers and medicine
In the future, when you are ill, you may be able to check out your symptoms with the computer before making an appointment to see the doctor. In the dialogue over the page, the patient is complaining of a pain in the stomach.

Computer	Imagine that I ask you to point out the area where you feel pain in your stomach – now, can the area best be indicated with one or two fingers, or with the flat of the hand? If with one or two fingers, press "Yes". If with the flat of the hand, press "No". If you don't understand, press "?".
Patient	No.
Computer	I expect you know where the navel is, but I want to be quite sure about this. Push "Yes" if you know where the navel is and "No" if you don't know.
Patient	Yes.
Computer	OK. Now, is the pain or discomfort, when you get it, mainly above the navel? Think carefully and push "Yes" or "No".
Patient	Yes.
Computer	Thank you. I now need to find out whether the pain or discomfort is to the left or right of your stomach, or whether it lies generally in the centre (which we call the midline) and I will ask you one or two questions about this. First of all does it lie on the midline? Push "Yes" if it does, and "No" if it doesn't.
Patient	Yes.
Computer	Would you say that you were eating normally these days? By normally, I mean do you have a reasonably good appetite? Press one button now.
Patient	Yes.
Computer	Well, you are being very helpful so far and I would now like to ask some more questions. I hope you still find this interesting. If you do, push the "Yes" button, but if you are getting bored, push the "No" button.
Patient	Yes.
Computer	In this present illness have you had any vomiting? Push "Yes" if you have and "No" if not.
Patient	Yes.
Computer	Could you tell me, when you vomit do you bring up food?
Patient	No.
Computer	Do you sometimes find that your mouth unexpectedly fills up with a fluid? Push "Yes" or "No", please.

52

Patient	Yes.
Computer	If you had to describe this liquid or fluid, would you say it was clear and tasted salty?
Patient	Yes.
Computer	Does the fluid ever have a bitter or acid taste? Press "Yes" if it does, and "No" if not.
Patient	Yes.
Computer	Thank you, we are getting on very well.

This is part of a computer program used at a clinic in Edinburgh that deals with stomach ailments. Many patients who have used the computer think it is as good as or better than a live doctor.

1 Do you think this type of program could be useful in finding out what disease a patient has?

2 Do you think it could ever be safe to allow computers to prescribe medicines?

3 Computers are impressive in what they can do, but they are, after all, just machines, and machines can go wrong. Try these improvisations about computers.

a Work with a partner. One of you will be the computer and the other the patient. The patient has a skin rash and is seeking advice on what to buy from the chemist. However, the computer gets stuck on a "Caring for your new baby" program. It only asks questions about feeding, bathing and changing the baby, such as "Do you use powdered milk?" Despite its 'malfunctions' the computer can interpret brief sentences from the patients as well as yes/no answers. Improvise an exchange of questions and answers. It might get interesting if you include nappy rash!

b Work in groups of four. A young surgeon and her assistant are performing an operation to remove a patient's appendix. They are operating under the guidance of a specialist and his assistant, who are performing a similar operation in another hospital. The two operations are linked by video. At a critical point the 'lines' get crossed with a *heart transplant* operation. The young surgeon is very much in awe of the specialist, and is afraid to criticise or ask too many questions. How would her assistant try to point out that all is not right? Remember – the patient's life may be put in danger.

Computers and education

A computer doctor we may be able to tolerate, but what about machines in place of teachers? Here is a short story about school in the future by Issac Asimov, called *The Fun They Had*.

Margie even wrote about it that night in her diary. On the page headed May 17, 2155, she wrote, "Today Tommy found a real book!"

It was a very old book. Margie's grandfather once said that when he was a little boy *his* grandfather told him that there was a time when all stories were printed on paper.

They turned the pages, which were yellow and crinkly, and it was awfully funny to read words that stood still instead of moving the way they were supposed to – on a screen, you know. And then when they turned back to the page before, it had the same words on it that it had had when they read it the first time.

"Gee," said Tommy, "what a waste. When you're through with the book, you just throw it away, I guess. Our television screen must have had a million books on it and it's good for plenty more. I wouldn't throw *it* away."

"Same with mine," said Margie. She was eleven and hadn't seen as many telebooks as Tommy had. He was thirteen.

She said, "Where did you find it?"

"In my house." He pointed without looking, because he was busy reading, "In the attic."

"What's it about?"

"School."

Margie was scornful. "School? What's there to write about school? I hate school." Margie always hated school, but now she hated it more than ever. The mechanical teacher had been giving her test after test in geography and she had been doing worse and worse until her mother had shaken her head sorrowfully and sent for the County Inspector. . . .

The inspector had smiled after he had finished and patted her head. He said to her mother, "It's not the little girl's fault, Mrs Jones. I think the geography sector was geared a little too quick. These things happen sometimes. I've slowed it up to an average ten-year level. Actually, the overall pattern of her progress is quite satisfactory." And he patted Margie's head again.

Margie was disappointed. She had been hoping they would take the teacher away altogether. They had once taken Tommy's teacher away for nearly a month because the history sector had blanked out completely.

So she said to Tommy, "Why would anyone write about school?"

Tommy looked at her with very superior eyes. "Because it's not our kind of school, stupid. This is the kind of school that they had hundreds and hundreds of years ago." He added loftily, pronouncing the word carefully, "*Centuries* ago."

Margie was hurt. "Well, I don't know what kind of school they had all that time ago." She read the book over his shoulder for a while, then said, "Anyway, they had a teacher."

"Sure they had a teacher, but it wasn't a *regular* teacher. It was a man."

"A man? How could a man be a teacher?"

"Well, he just told the boys and girls things and gave them homework and asked them questions."

"A man isn't smart enough."

"Sure he is. My father knows as much as my teacher."

"He can't. A man can't know as much as a teacher."

"He knows almost as much as I, betcha."

Margie wasn't prepared to dispute that. She said, "I wouldn't want a strange man in my house to teach me."

Tommy screamed with laughter. "You don't know much, Margie. The teacher's didn't live in the house. They had a special building and all the kids went there."

"And all the kids learned the same thing?"

"Sure, if they were the same age."

"But my mother says a teacher has to be adjusted to fit the mind of each boy and girl it teaches and that each kid has to be taught differently."

"Just the same, they didn't do it that way then. If you don't like it, you don't have to read the book."

"I didn't say I didn't like it," said Margie quickly. She wanted to read about those funny schools.

They weren't half finished when Margie's mother called, "Margie! School!"

Margie looked up. "Not yet, mamma."

"Now," said Mrs Jones. "And its probably time for Tommy, too."

Margie said to Tommy, "Can I read the book some more with you after school?"

"Maybe," he said, nonchalantly. He walked away whistling, the dusty old book tucked beneath his arm.

Margie went into the school-room. It was right next to her bedroom, and the mechanical teacher was awaiting for her. It was always on at the same time every day except Saturday and Sunday, because her mother said little girls learned better if they learned at regular hours.

The screen was lit up, and it said: "Today's arithmetic lesson in on the addition of proper fractions. Please insert yesterday's homework in the proper slot."

Margie did so with a sigh. She was thinking about the old schools they had when her grandfather's grandfather was a little boy. All the kids from the whole neighbourhood came, laughing and shouting in the schoolyard, sitting together in the schoolroom, going home together at the end of the day. They learned the same things so they could help one another on the homework and talk about it.

1 Work with a partner to play Tommy and Margie. You have just come across a derelict school in a distant part of town. What can you see through the windows? Explore the building. Do you recognise anything you read about in Tommy's book? Has anything been left behind that tells you what life was like in the school?

2 What might Margie write in her diary on the day she visited the old school?

3 Create a scene in which Margie, as she writes her diary, begins to hear sounds of the school . . . snatches of conversations, lessons, games . . . voices fading in and out. These school 'echoes' could be created in groups of five or six and recorded on a tape recorder. Try to create the effect on playback of voices in Margie's imagination.

4 The school scenes could be brought to life. This would be a good opportunity for the whole class to work together on one improvisation. Would Margie enter the scenes in school? If so, would the children in the school be able to see and hear her?

5 Suppose that on another visit to the derelict school Margie finds a faded exercise book. Inside the cover is a pupil's name, and this pupil grows into a real person in Margie's imagination.

Work in pairs. How would Margie talk to her imaginary friend? Margie could show this friend into her own schoolroom, where they could both talk about their experiences of school.

What would happen if one day Margie's mother overheard her speaking to her imaginary friend?

6 If you now bring together Asimov's story and your improvisations, you have the elements for making an exciting play. Some scenes could be taken directly from the story – the visit of the County Inspector, for example – and others could be developed from related situations. Margie may visit her grandfather, or she may have an argument with her mother about her schoolwork. These scenes could be interwoven with scenes in the derelict school and with the imaginary friend. Try not to fix the dialogue and sequence of scenes too soon. Keep the process of working out the play as active and experimental as possible.

Who is in control?

What do you think were the intentions of the planners when they built Rose Street Development? Were they interested in creating a living environment to suit the needs of everyone in it? Or might there have been a more sinister purpose? After all, a large building could be used to control people's behaviour. Also, the machines that spread information to the citizens could be used to collect information *on them*.

There are no such suggestions in the play itself, and indeed all the machines in the building break down all the time. But could there be another more sinister story *behind* the story of Arty and his friends?

In his book *Nineteen Eighty-Four*, George Orwell describes a vision of society completely controlled by the government, which keeps a careful watch on its citizens at all times.

Behind Winston's back the voice from the telescreen was still babbling away about pig iron and the overfulfilment of the Ninth Three-Year Plan. The telescreen received and transmitted simultaneously. Any sound that Winston made, above the level of a very low whisper, would be picked up by it; moreover, so long as he remained within the field of vision which the metal plaque commanded, he could be seen as well as heard. There was of course no way of knowing whether you were being watched at any given moment. How often, or on what system, the Thought Police plugged in on any individual wire was guesswork. It was even conceivable that they watched everybody all the time. But at any rate they could plug in your wire whenever they wanted to. You had to live – did live, from habit that became instinct – in the assumption that every sound you made was overheard, and, except in darkness, every movement scrutinized.

Winston kept his back turned to the telescreen. It was safer; though, as he well knew, even a back can be revealing. A kilometre away the Ministry of Truth, his place of work, towered vast and white above the grimy landscape. This, he thought with a sort of vague distaste – this was London. He tried to squeeze out some childhood memory that should tell him whether London had always been quite like this.

1 Imagine that at the time the Rose Street Development exists, the country is controlled by an authoritarian government as in *Nineteen Eighty-Four*. Write a report submitted by the Thought Police to the central computer, telling it about the Gang's journey to the street. What special comments would the Police make about individual members of the gang? How would the Thought Police regard the Level Tenners?

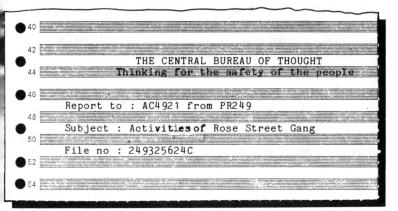

```
  40
  42
              THE CENTRAL BUREAU OF THOUGHT
  44         Thinking for the safety of the people

  46
       Report to : AC4921 from PR249
  48
       Subject : Activities of Rose Street Gang
  50
       File no : 249325624C
  52
  54
```

2 Lance's Factcentre is on the blink. In anger, he has keyed in some random numbers, and the following information has appeared on the screen: TIME 10.30 SUSPECT 174266100 (COOPER, A.) LEFT HOME AT 09.25 AND MET SUSPECT 042863100 (HOPKINS, B.) AT 09.35. BOTH SUSPECTS MEET REGULARLY. COOPER SUSPECTED OF LEADING VISITS TO THE STREET AND MISSING CLASSES AT EDUCATION CENTRE. RETURNED HOME 14.30. BOTH SUSPECTS NOW ON CAMERAS 7521 AND 7430 ZONE A. SUGGEST CONTINUE SURVEILLANCE

In groups of six, act out a scene where Lance explains this to Arty and the Gang, at a meeting they have arranged on the walkway.

3 The Gang has found a quicker route to the street, and their visits have become more frequent and adventurous. Many friends have joined them. They are all very fed-up with life inside the Rose Street Development.

Work in groups of six. Arty and Beowulf are called to appear before the Committee of Law and Order. The Committee asks them questions about the group and what they do in Rose Street. Role-play the interrogation.

4 Now divide into pairs. A few days later, Arty finds a boy he has never seen before hiding on the walkway. The boy, Pericles, is a fugitive from another building, another development. What is he running from? What does Arty do? What happens to them? Act out their story.

5 Unknown to Arty, Pericles is carrying a tiny electronic bug implanted under his skin. The signal it transmits allows the police to follow his movements.

Two days later, Arty is once again called before the Committee of Law and Order. What questions does the Committee ask him this time? Does it decide anything? In groups, act out this part of the story.

If you would like to explore the *Nineteen Eighty-Four* theme by computer simulation, try a program called 'Big Brother' (produced by CLASS). As well as being exciting to play, it provides a useful way in to reading Orwell's book.

RELATED READING

Natfact 7 by John Tully (Methuen)
Devil on my Back by Monica Hughes (Julia MacRae Books)
Crisis on Conshelf Ten by Monica Hughes (Hamish Hamilton)
Fahrenheit 451 by Ray Bradbury (Collins Educational – Cascades edition)
The Guardians, The Lotus Caves, Wild Jack, all by John Christopher (Hamish Hamilton)
The Weathermonger by Peter Dickinson (Victor Gollancz)
Riddley Walker by Russell Hoban (Picador)
Children of the Dust by Louise Lawrence (Bodley Head)
Andra by Louise Lawrence (Macmillan)
Brother in the Land by Robert Swindells (Oxford University Press)
The Machine Stops by E. M. Forster in *Strange Universe* (Blackie)